Funny Money:

More Fun with Clichés!

Jayne Pearl

Written by
Jayne A. Pearl

Illustrated by
Mat Bevilacqua

Library of Congress Cataloging-in-Publication Data
Pearl, Jayne A., 1954 –
Bevilacqua, Mat, 1989 –
LCCN:
2021913235

First Printing: August 2021
12345678910

Typesetting by Authors First Self Publishing
Printed in the United States of America

ALLLRIGHT BOOKS
ISBN: 978-1-7366715-9-7 (paperback)
ISBN: 978-1-7366715-5-9 (ebook)

Dedication

To my sisters, Robin Pearl and Ellen Pollen—JP.

and

To my wife, Bianca Bevilacqua—MB.

As the family that plays together stays together, may we always continue to laugh and love!

Every week, little Bit Coyne went to the grocery store with Mama Penny Coyne and Papa Buck Coyne. During one shopping trip, Bit was surprised when Mama Penny exclaimed, "Everything here **costs an arm and a leg!**"

"Ew!" Bit Coyne said. "Do we really have to give them an arm and a leg?"

Papa Buck said, "That's just another way to say it costs a lot of money!"

"Then why didn't you just say so?" Bit Coyne asked.

"Don't worry, little Bit," Mama Penny answered. "We can afford to buy what we need. We can even pay with **cold cash!**"

"Wait. What? Is there a teeny freezer in your pocketbook?" Bit Coyne asked.

"Of course not, silly!" Mama Penny laughed. "I meant we will pay with dollars and coins instead of a credit card."

"Then why didn't you just say so?" Bit asked.

Bit Coyne watched her father check price tags on packages of pasta, peas and peanut butter. **"Money doesn't grow on trees!"** he complained.

"Money trees?" Bit asked. "Where would we find money seeds?"

Papa Buck smiled. "That's another way to say we work hard to earn money to pay for things we need."

"Then why didn't you just say so?" little Bit asked.

Mama Penny was reading labels on two cereal boxes, to see which one cost less. "These sure cost **a pretty penny**," she said.

Bit Coyne was surprised. "You are the only pretty Penny I know, Mama!"

"That's very funny," Mama Penny said. "'Pretty penny' actually means 'a lot money,' silly!"

"Then why didn't you just say so?" Bit Coyne asked.

Papa Buck tried to explain. "Your mother means we have to **pay through the nose.**"

As Bit Coyne tried to imagine her mama paying through her nose, Papa Buck added, "That's yet another way to say all these groceries cost a lot of money," he said.

"Then why didn't you just say so?" little Bit asked.

At the checkout line, the cashier rang up everything in the Coyne family's shopping cart.

When Mama Penny saw the total amount, she opened her purse and said, "Well, I guess **we can kiss our money goodbye!**"

Papa Buck said to his wife, "Now you'll confuse Bit even more." Then he told Bit, "Mama means it's hard to spend so much money all at once."

"Then why didn't you just say so?" Bit Coyne asked.

As they left the store with their groceries, Papa Buck explained, "I guess all these funny-money expressions are more interesting ways that people say things."

"Are you **trying to pass the buck**, Papa?" Bit Coyne asked mischievously.

Papa Buck and Mama Penny both giggled as they loaded bags of food into their car.

"So you DO understand about using expressions to describe things?" Papa Buck asked.

Bit Coyne nodded. "I kind of knew what you meant all along. You might say I was just **'pulling your leg.'** And that's another way to say I was tricking you!"

Mama Penny and Papa Buck said at the same time: "Then why didn't you just say so?"

In Case You're Wondering....

According to Merriam Webster,
the definition of *cliché* is:
"A trite phrase or expression."

~

Clearly, clichés have gotten a bad rap. For a good reason! Initially, they expressed something in a funny, clever or particularly visual way, but they became so popular that everyone started using them. Like jokes you hear over and over and over, today many clichés no longer seem so funny or clever.

But sometimes oldies can be goodies. When you try to envision the literal meaning of an old idiom or expression, the cliché acquires some new cache—some combination of absurd, silly, and ridiculous.

Many of us use clichés all the time without thinking about it. To prove this, *keep your ears peeled* (LOL) and you are bound to hear a whole lot of clichés—like, all the time. Sometimes the meaning is obvious, but when pressed to explain it, you may have a hard time.

So in case your little ones (or you, dear reader!) need a hint or two, on the following pages you will find each cliché in *Funny Money*, followed by some questions you can ask your children to help them guess the meaning of that cliché. Then you will see the origins of each phrase.

Paying an arm and a leg

Prompts: Do you think anyone actually pays for things with a real arm or leg? If so, would that arm or leg be worth a lot or a little? What do you think "it costs an arm and a leg" really means?

Actual meaning: To pay, give, or do whatever is necessary to achieve or buy something that you want or need.

Possible sources: This cliché became popular during the 1930s, probably from American criminals' slang phrase, "if it takes a leg" (in other words, even at the cost of a leg, to express a desperate situation).

Paying with cold cash

Prompts: Is money actually cold? How would it get that way? Does the temperature of a coin or dollar bill make it worth any more or less? What do you think "paying with cold cash" means?

Actual meaning: Paying for something with dollar bills and coins instead of a check, credit or debit card or an electronic method.

Possible sources: Merchants and traders used to handle coins with high gold and silver content, which were warm and soft. Because they wore out quickly, eventually coins began to be made of colder, harder metals—cold cash!

Money doesn't grow on trees

Prompts: How do people usually get enough money to buy things? Is it easy or hard to earn money? What do you think "money doesn't grow on trees" means?

Actual meaning: Money should not be wasted because it can't be replenished as easily as leaves that grow on trees.

Possible sources: One theory: In ancient Carthage, as early as 146 BCE, commercial banks began to issue promissory notes made from parchment or leather. But it wasn't until more than 2,000 years later, that one of the earliest print references to this cliché appeared (in 1891), in Boston's *Daily Advertiser*.

Paying a pretty Penny

Prompts: Do you think the picture of Abraham Lincoln on pennies is pretty? What might make a penny pretty? What do you think paying "a pretty penny" means?

Actual meaning: This expression doesn't mean a penny is attractive, but that money is precious. Something that costs a pretty penny means it costs a lot of money.

Possible sources: The first known written use of this phrase was in a 1712 issue of a London publication, *The Spectator*. In Britain (at that time), a penny had much greater purchasing power than today's American penny.

Cliché	Prompts and Circumstances

Paying through the nose

Prompts: When someone sneezes, could money really come out of their nose? If something you want to buy costs a lot of money, how do you think that would feel? What do you think "paying through the nose" means?

Actual meaning: When we spend a lot of money, if can feel as uncomfortable as pulling something out of our nose!

Possible sources: The origin may allude to a Danish "nose tax" imposed in the 9th century, referring to the amount required each person ("per head" or "per nose") to pay. Another theory is based on the 17th century use of the British slang word "rhino," for money. This led to the phrase "nosebleed" to mean being bled dry of money.

Kissing your money goodbye

Prompts: How do you feel when you kiss someone or something goodbye, especially when you don't know when you will see them again? What do you think "kissing your money goodbye" means?

Actual meaning: To spend on or invest in something that is likely to be a waste of money; to lose or end something suddenly.

Possible sources: Unknown

Cliché	Prompts and Circumstances

Passing the Buck

Prompts: Have you ever been blamed for a mistake you did not make? Or have you blamed someone for a mistake that you made? What do you think "passing the buck" means?

Actual meaning: To shift responsibility by blaming someone who is innocent of some mistake or crime.

Possible sources: This term comes from the U.S. in the 19th-century, to refer to the next player to be the dealer in a poker game, indicated by passing a piece of buckshot or a knife with a buckhorn handle to that player. In 1949, President Harry Truman had a sign on his Oval Office desk that read: "The buck stops here," saying he would take responsibility for his policies.

Pulling your leg

Prompts: Have you ever pretended, as a joke, that something was true when you knew it was a lie? What do you think "pulling your leg" means?

Actual meaning: To tease or trick someone by trying to convince them something is true that is not really true.

Possible sources: Two possible sources: 1) thieves tripping people before they robbed them; or 2) when, in the past, people were hanged, friends or family members might pull their legs hard so they died faster and suffered less.

Sources:

• *The Dictionary of Clichés* by James Rogers; Ballentine Books, 1985.

• *Most Comprehensive Origins of Clichés, Proverbs, and Figurative Expressions (Vol. 1)* by Stanley J. St. Clair; St. Clair Publications: 2013.

• *The Oxford English Dictionary*, Oxford University Press: 2021

• "The Oxford Etymologist" (by Anatoly Liberman) column (https://blog.oup.com)

• https://answers.yahoo.com/question/

• http://idioms.thefreedictionary.com

• https://www.theidioms.com/

• https://knowyourphrase.com/

• https://www.lexico.com

• http://www.wikipedia.org

Acknowledgements

Special thanks to Hilary Salk for her support, encouragement, and enthusiasm.

We appreciate the many thoughtful comments and suggestions from Bianca Bevilacqua, Cheryl Block, Sarina Ergas, Allan Feldman, Ryan and Cynthia Hommel, Sheryl Kaplan, Robin Pearl, Ellen Pollen, Joan Robb, Harriet Rogers, Terry Rooney and Ellen Seh.

We are so grateful for all your ideas and for sharing lots of belly laughs along the way.

About the Author

Jayne Pearl is a journalist and entertaining speaker, focusing on family business and financial parenting. Her nonfiction books, including *Kids and Money* (Bloomberg Press) and *Kids, Wealth, and Consequences* (Wiley), present original and proven techniques for instilling positive financial values, skills and discipline in children and young adults.

She also writes poetry and has created a series of humorous children's books, including *Dog Days of Summer: Fun with Clichés*, and the forthcoming *Following My Heart: Yet More Fun with Clichés!* and *Planting Kisses: Still More Fun with Clichés!*

Jayne has also been a big sister for more than twelve years with the Big Brothers Big Sisters of Hampshire County program, and volunteers at Center for New Americans, helping recent immigrants adjust to living in the U.S. She lives in Western Massachusetts.

About the Illustrator

Mat Bevilacqua has produced large, colorful murals outdoors, as well as smaller commissions both public and private. He combines elements of design, painting, and illustration. As Mat's Instagram portfolio (@ MatBev) reveals, his work is vibrant and tactile, resonating with a strong sense of color and form, working in unison. Mat resides in Providence, Rhode Island with his wife, Bianca, their toddler son, and their Siberian husky, Ralph.

Keep Your Eyes Peeled!

Coming Soon:

Planting Kisses: Still More Fun with Clichés!

Following My Heart: Yet More Fun with Clichés!

CPSIA information can be obtained
at www.ICGtesting.com
Printed in the USA
BVHW051337130921
616278BV00002B/24

9 781736 671597